Dear Friends,

"Stewie" the water safety duck was created in loving memory of our son, Stew Leonard III. While on a family vacation in 1989, our 21-month-old son, Stewie, ventured into the pool unnoticed. Within minutes, a house-wide search ensued – that's when we noticed a yellow t-shirt floating in the pool. We dove in, quickly got him out of the water, and immediately began performing CPR. But it was too late.

We later learned that drowning is the most common cause of death in children under five years old. Many of the drowning accidents among children occur in friends' or neighbors' pools.

In 1990, our family founded the Stew Leonard III Water Safety Foundation to help promote water safety awareness. The Foundation has helped to raise millions of dollars for water safety awareness and education, including swimming lesson scholarships and lifeguard training.

We read every book we could find about water safety and children, and were surprised that there were no fun, instructional guides targeted to kids. We thought creating a character like "Stewie the Duck" would make wearing a life vest cool, make it fun for children to learn water safety lessons, and be another way we could make a difference.

If you would like to contact the Stew Leonard III Water Safety Foundation, please visit www.stewietheduck.org. Please also download our free *Stewie the Duck Learns to Swim* app on iTunes, Android/Google Play, and Kindle HD.

We hope that you, your family, and all of the children in your life enjoy Stewie the Duck Learns to Swim.

Swim Safe!

— Kim + Stew Leonard, Jr.

Dedication

To our four beautiful daughters: Blake, Ryann, Chase, and Madison. "One day they will know that they were our merchants of hope."
A special thanks to our Board members past and present, Tom Anrico, Rich Burghoff, Andrew Colton, Patty Guthman, Rich Lung, Doreen Miner, Les Slater, Nicole Weiss and Meghan Bell.

— Kim + Stew Leonard, Jr.

Stewie the Duck Learns to Swim

by Kim and
Stew Leonard
with Dr. Lawrence E. Shapiro

Illustrated by Vicky Lowe

Stewie-the-Duck wanted to swim more than anything in the world. He wanted to splash, and dive, and swim from one end of the pool to the other!

One hot day, Stewie could hear the big ducks swimming in the pool. He wanted to go swimming with them really, really badly!

5

But the big ducks knew that Stewie was not ready to swim by himself.

"Go away, Stewie! You're a little duck. You can't come near the water until you learn to swim!" said his older sister **Blake**.

"Go away, Stewie!" said his neighbor **Ryann**. "You're too little to swim by yourself. You need a life vest!"

6

"Go away, Stewie. You don't know how to swim. You need a grown-up to watch you!" said his friend **Chase**.

7

"But I **am** a big duck! Look, I can draw!" said Stewie.

"Stewie, you can't come swimming until you know all the rules!
Listen, I'll sing them to you," said **Blake**.

(Sing to the tune of Twinkle, Twinkle Little Star - music page 32)

9

"But I **am** a big duck! Look, I can ride a two wheel bike and say my ABC's!" said Stewie.

"Stewie, you know you can't come swimming until you've learned all the rules!" quacked Chase.

"Let's all sing them together!" said **Ryann**.

Don't jump in 'til you learn to swim.
Cover your chest with a safe life vest.
A grown-up must watch you in the pool.
You'll be safe if you learn these rules!
Don't jump in 'til you learn to swim.
Stewie the duck wants you safe like him!

Stewie was very unhappy because he couldn't go
in the pool with the big ducks. He went inside
to tell his Mom and Dad.

"My friends won't let me go swimming with them because
they say I'm not a big duck, and I don't know all the rules,"
said Stewie.

Stewie started to cry.

"Your friends are **<u>RIGHT</u>**! You must **<u>NEVER</u>** go near the
water until you know the water safety rules. Do you want
to learn them now?" asked Stewie's Mom and Dad.

"Yes! I really, really want to learn all the rules!" shouted Stewie.

"The first rule is you
must **LEARN** to swim.
We'll go and sign you up for swimming lessons and
meet your instructor," said Stewie's Mom.

"The second rule is you must **ALWAYS** wear a life vest. It helps you float and will keep you on top of the water while you learn to swim," said Stewie's Dad.

"The third and **<u>MOST IMPORTANT</u>** rule is you must ALWAYS have a grown-up watch you around the water and to ask permission before going near the water," said Stewie's Dad.

Stewie finished his swimming lessons.
He promised his Mom and Dad that
he would never go near the water without
them and always wear his life vest.

One day Stewie was outside playing
and he heard the big ducks swimming
in the pool. He ran inside. "Mom, Dad
can I go swimming with the big ducks,
PLEEEEASE?" begged Stewie.

"Stewie, do you remember all the rules?" asked Stewie's Mom and Dad. "Yes, I do! I do!" shouted Stewie.

"Let's hear you sing the rules," said Stewie's Mom.

Don't jump in 'til you learn to swim.
Cover your chest with a safe life vest.
A grown-up must watch you in the pool.
You'll be safe if you learn these rules.
Don't jump in 'til you learn to swim.
Stewie the duck wants you safe like him.

Stewie and his Dad went back outside
to go swimming with the big ducks.

"Hey, guys, I've learned to swim! I'm wearing my life vest
and my Dad is going to watch me. Can I swim with you now?"

"Sure!" said **Blake**.

"Come on in!" quacked **Ryann**.

"I'm going to splash you!" yelled **Chase**.

Just as Stewie was about to go in swimming,
he noticed baby **Madison** running towards the pool.

Stewie stood in front of baby **Madison**
and blocked her way.

"STOP! You don't know how to swim and you're not wearing a
life vest. Plus, you have to learn the water safety rules,"
shouted Stewie.

Stewie's Dad walked over and put his arm around Stewie and said, "Thank you so much for stopping baby Madison from going into the pool; being SAFE around the water is the **MOST IMPORTANT** thing!

I have a surprise for you!" said Stewie's Dad.

Let's all sing the water safety song. . .

Some Water Safety TIPS for Parents

1. ALWAYS HAVE YOUR KIDS WEAR FLOTATION DEVICES WHEN NEAR THE WATER. BUT, DON'T RELY ON THEM!

2. ALWAYS DESIGNATE A WATER WATCHER AND PUT YOUR CELL PHONE DOWN!

3. TEACH YOUR CHILD TO FLOAT ON THEIR BACK AND MAKE A LONG TERM COMMITMENT TO TEACHING THEM HOW TO SWIM.

The water is a wonderful place for fun and exercise, but safety must always be the first priority.

Rob Polley - President, SwimAmerica, Norwalk, CT

SwimAmerica is a nationally certified learn-to-swim program offered by the American Swimming Coaches Association

"¡Este libro pudiera salvarle la vida a su hijo!"
— Greg deSablon, YMCA, Yonkers, NY

El Patito Stewie Aprende a nadar

escrito por Kim y Stew Leonard, Jr. con la ayuda del Dr. Lawrence E. Shapiro

La primera guía de seguridad en el agua

Ilustrado por Vicky Lowe

Also available in Spanish

Thank You
to all our sponsors!

Visit us at...
Stewietheduck.org

Stewie-the-Duck Song

sung to Twinkle, Twinkle Little Star